D1631960

A DORLING KINDERSLEY BOOK

Managing Editor Bridget Gibbs
Senior Designer Claire Jones
Designer Lisa Hollis
DTP Designer Kim Browne
Production Katy Holmes
Photography Dave King

First published in Great Britain in 1997
by Dorling Kindersley Limited,
A Penguin Company
80 Strand, London WC2R 0RL

Visit us on the World Wide Web at http://www.dk.com

ISBN 0-7513-7095-9

Colour reproduction by G.R.B. Graphica, Verona
Printed and bound in China by Sun Fung Offset Binding Company Limited.

Acknowledgements
Dorling Kindersley would like to thank the following manufacturer
for permission to photograph copyright material:
Ty Inc. for "Toffee" the dog

Dorling Kindersley would like to thank
Barbara Owen, Vera Jones, Dave King and Steve Gorton
for their help in producing this book.

What is P.B. Bear doing?

LEE DAVIS

LONDON, NEW YORK, MUNICH,
PARIS, MELBOURNE, DELHI

Can you find me on each page?

P.B. Bear gets out of bed.
He's got a busy day ahead!

It's eight o'clock. What will he do?

Turn the page and
he'll show you . . .

It's nine o'clock. What will he do?

Turn the page and he'll show you . . .

It's twelve o'clock. What will he do?

Turn the page and he'll show you . . .

It's three o'clock. What will he do?

Turn the page and he'll show you . . .

It's five o'clock. What will he do?

Turn the page and he'll show you . . .

It's six o'clock. What will he do?

Turn the page and he'll show you . . .

It's seven o'clock. What will he do?

Turn the page and he'll show you . . .